MW00609595

DREAM LIFE PLANNER

Move From Tired and Overwhelmed to Free and Empowered!

NOELLE L. PETERSON MED

Copyright © 2022 by Noelle L. Peterson MEd

ISBN: 978-1-64810-150-2

All rights reserved. No part of this book may be reproduced mechanically, electronically, virtually, or by any other means, including photocopying without written permission of the publisher. It is illegal to copy this book, post it to any website or distribute it by any other means without permission from the publisher.

Published by Perfect Publishing Co.

PREFACE

Why did I write this?

I was overwhelmed with all the tasks expected of us. I was a missionary wife while going to college. As I grew in my role as a wife and mother, I was also growing in leadership. I knew early on that I wanted to help others grow. I assisted in a missionary school, helped guide volunteers at church, and took every leadership class I could. In college, when I had a choice of topics, I navigated to leadership courses.

My passion is to help women be all that they can be. I want everyone to have their dream life and not to struggle with the tribulations of this world.

I enjoy building relationships with in many industries. I was a small group leader, youth leader, and women's ministry leader for many years. Being a sounding board was natural. We all need to talk and to be heard. Knowing when to give advice and support is a skill that I have tuned through different experiences.

I was overwhelmed with all the books that one can read. Over the years, I have also read and listened to books about business growth, personal growth, mindset, leadership and others. They seemed to miss the mark. Encouraged by my husband, I decided to create a workbook with clear instructions and inspiring activities to encourage you to take actions towards an abundant life.

Working through these concepts has helped me become free from the constraints and expectations of this world. I am empowered to be the woman God created me to be. We are made in his image, to be lights in this world.

It took a couple of weeks, but I finally sat down and started putting words on the page. I wanted to create a workbook that was laid out in a way that made sense to me and included enough information to help you, the reader, understand the concepts, as well as know how to complete each activity.

I hope I have done just this, and that you are able to follow along, and that as you complete the activities you relish in the concepts and plans that you'll put in place to bring an abundant life to you.

DREAM LIFE PLANNER • NOELLE L. PETERSON MED

Introduction

This planner is designed to help you understand who you are and who you want to become. We'll evaluate your current situation, your dream for what you ultimately want and develop steps for getting there. Understanding where you are and picturing where you want to go, will allow you to develop the path to get there.

It is not the end goal that we ultimately want. We need to become the person worthy of that goal. The journey that we create will allow us to grow into the person worthy of all that we dream to be. We may end up at a different place, but we will be a better version of ourselves and the goal or dream will be even better than we ever imagined.

While I have organized these activities in this order, it is not required to be done as such. Do the activities that make sense to you and come back to the ones that need more of your time.

Work through these activity pages to work through who you are, who you want to be, and how you are going get there. Afterward, if you're interested, I'd love to hear from you and how you succeeded this year. You can find me on Facebook and Instagram at @n2r2peterson.

WHERE ARE YOU NOW?

Who are you today? This may seem unnecessary but when we try to say who we are it is not always an easy answer. I personally struggle with this question. Rate your current state in the applicable areas below. 1 being you are content in the area but do not do anything to improve, and 10 being you're actively working on improving in that area. Do not stress or take too much time, we're just evaluating for now.

Skills/Knowledge

| 1 | 2 | 3 | 4 | 5 | 6 | 7 | 8 | 9 | 10 |

Physical

| 1 | 2 | 3 | 4 | 5 | 6 | 7 | 8 | 9 | 10 |

Family

| 1 | 2 | 3 | 4 | 5 | 6 | 7 | 8 | 9 | 10 |

Job

| 1 | 2 | 3 | 4 | 5 | 6 | 7 | 8 | 9 | 10 |

Financial

| 1 | 2 | 3 | 4 | 5 | 6 | 7 | 8 | 9 | 10 |

DREAM LIFE PLANNER • NOELLE L. PETERSON MED

Emotional

    1   2   3   4   5   6   7   8   9   10

Relationship

    1   2   3   4   5   6   7   8   9   10

Social

    1   2   3   4   5   6   7   8   9   10

Recreational

    1   2   3   4   5   6   7   8   9   10

Spiritual

    1   2   3   4   5   6   7   8   9   10

Why It Matters

Regardless of who we are and who we want to be, we must know why we want to get there. What is your purpose? Simon Sinek says, "people buy why you do what you do, more than what you do." Why do you get up in the morning? What keeps you going? Take a few moments to write down what comes to mind for these questions.

1. Why do you want your life to be different?

2. Why do you want / need to change?

3. What do you want your future to look like?

4. Why is that future important to you?

5. What is the cost of ignoring that dream?

6. What is the worst thing that could happen if you try? If you commit to follow that dream?

7. What do you want to create?

8. I will not give up because....

9. Why is that important?

10. Which answer touched your heart or felt right in your gut?

11. Write your final "why" statement. (To _contribution_ so that _impact,_ i.e., "To inspire people to do the things that inspire them so that, together, we can change our world.")

WHERE DO YOU SPEND YOUR TIME?

I can relate to feeling there is never enough time in the day. Not having enough time is one of the most common excuses made for not taking action on their dreams or accomplishing their to do list. Unfortunately, it can last a lifetime unless you schedule time.

That's why this evaluation is a great tool. It's a perfect way to make time to fit in what you need to accomplish.

Use the next page to evaluate your current schedule and how you spend your time.

Remember how they say you can figure out a person's priorities by looking at their checkbook? You can evaluate your schedule by looking at your calendar. Where do you spend your time?

If you struggle to complete this, take a day or a week and track your activities. Mark down everything in your electronic or paper calendar, or even on a sheet of paper. Carry it around with you and make notes for each hour on what you did or how the hour was spent.

Once you have a clear idea of your schedule, then you can evaluate the activities on the calendar and what can be eliminated or adjusted to allow time for activities that will elevate your plan to reach your dream.

It can be hard to say "no" to people or activities, especially if they have valuable influence on you or those around you. Let me give you a new perspective.

I encourage you to know your priorities and then evaluate the activity requests against them. If they don't fit in with your priorities and plans for the week, month or year, saying "no" to them really means you are saying yes to your priorities. For example, if it is a priority to spend Thursday nights with the ladies, then a request to meet a coworker for dinner on Thursday night is an easy "no." The coworker is a valuable time but it can be done another time.

It's ok to start small. Look for small moments of time, or a few nights a week, where you can block out time to focus on a goal you'll draft later. Carve out this time in your calendar. You deserve to take care of yourself and to follow your dreams.

SCHEDULE PLAN

There are some things that we do out of habit or routine each day. Sometimes we're on autopilot and we even forget they are part of our daily schedule.

In your schedule evaluation, the goal is to find patterns for using time and identify activities that can be removed or adjusted to allow time for working on your dream. What are your priorities?

Morning routine....

Afternoon routine....

Evening routine ...

What things are you going to stop doing so that the time can be invested in your dream?	What things are you going to do that moves you closer to your dream?
1.	
2.	
3.	

LIMITING BELIEFS

We must understand that we all have some beliefs that limit us from achieving great things. We develop beliefs throughout our lives that help us push forward as well as some that hold us back. A limiting belief is something that you believe to be true but hinders you somehow from becoming who you want to be. These beliefs may:

- Hold you back from making different choices in your life
- Keep you from seeing the different opportunities presented to you each day
- Prevent you from seeing your own gifts or accepting the gifts offered to you, or
- Keep you stuck focusing on the negative aspect of your circumstances.

One of the challenges with limiting beliefs is most of us don't think we have them and they can be hard to spot. Some of these beliefs are things like:

- "I am not worthy"
- "I am not _____ enough"
- "There isn't enough _____"
- "I can't"
- "Why try"
- "I don't want others to think_____"[1]

---

1   https://www.habitsforwellbeing.com/what-are-your-biggest-limiting-beliefs/

I want to tell you right now that there are plenty of clients, plenty of ideas, and plenty of money for everyone to do what they dream to do. There is no limit to things you want to do. There are plenty of people in the world that, even if you are doing something someone else is doing, they won't do it the same as you. You are unique in your talents and abilities.

Let me tell you a story. When my grandson was young, his mom was trying to get him to give grandpa a hug. She quickly said that if you don't hug him, I will and then you can't. This was as if grandpa only had a single hug to give that afternoon. Now, we all know that our hugs are endless.

The world is the same. There is an abundance of ideas. There are a lot of people in this world that, even if you do the same as someone else, there are plenty of businesses to support. Remember we buy from the why, not the what. People will buy from you for you, not for what you sell.

To debunk these limiting beliefs, write down statements to the contrary that are true. Put these in a place you'll see them daily. Read them aloud in the morning and night. Reprogram your subconscious to the contrary.

- "I am worthy of _____"
- "I am _____ enough"
- "There is enough _____ in the world"

Take a moment and write down some limiting beliefs you have, and then write down the more positive alternative.

Example:

I am just a mom I am an amazing mom and an influence in the lives of my family

Belief #1   **Better Alternative**

Belief #2   **Better Alternative**

Belief #3   **Better Alternative**

Belief #4   **Better Alternative**

DREAM LIFE PLANNER • NOELLE L. PETERSON MED

I AM

We talk to ourselves all day every day. We say positive and negative things without even realizing it. Many of these thoughts don't cross our conscious filter, they are just there. These will take some work to reprogram. We need to consciously make statements that change our subconscious to be more helpful in our thinking and planning.

Take some time and write out some reprogramming statements. These can be the same as the limiting belief rewrites, but I encourage you to write specific statements to reprogram your subconscious on how great you are..

I am...

Examples:
    I am loved
    I am beautiful
    I am smart
    I am worthy
    I am successful

I am…

I am…

I am…

GRATITUDE

Thinking of who we are, we need to be
grateful for what we have and how far
we have come. We didn't get this far in life without some work and some key
people in our lives. Take some time to be grateful for what you are and have.
Think of the people currently and previously in your life. Think of things that have
happened to you to bring you to today. Think of things that make you smile.

Nothing new can come into your life unless
you are grateful for what you already have.
Michael Bernard

Today, I'm grateful for...

VISION BOARD

The real power is to take those words and add imagery that penetrates your brain. When we create an image and attach an emotion it is stored in a different part of the brain that controls our subconscious actions.

The power in a vision board allows images of the dream to move beyond the language part of the brain. The subconscious doesn't understand words, it doesn't understand time, so a memory from the past or the future has equal influence. This part of the brain doesn't see a difference between a real experience or an experience that was vividly imagined. When you take your dreams, the desires of who you want to be, and you visualize yourself working where you want, doing the things you want, using the things that you want to have, it has a powerful impact on the brain. Take this a step further and add positive emotion to the image. It will put a stronghold on the memory.

The more visual and emotional elements that you can attach or anchor to these images of your future self, the more your brain and the universe will collaborate to help you accomplish them.

You will be inspired to take action, because your future self will be demanding it of your present self, and then you are in exciting territory.

I highly recommend, you take some time and cut and paste images from magazines, Pinterest, or google and create yourself a vision board. Whether it is an 8x11 piece of paper, a digital Pinterest board, or a large poster board, create your future self in images and hang it in your home or office where it can motivate you daily.

Visioneering

When dreaming of your future self, answer these five questions. It is helpful to make your answers concrete achievements instead of statements like, "I am successful." You should try to make statements like "I am a person of good reputation," "I have a residual income of $5000 a month." It is important to write these in present tense, as if they have already happened.

Use the chart below or use a separate piece of paper and write them down. Don't worry about getting them perfect. Write some answers and then you can adjust them later.

Before I die, I want...

1. Who do you want to BE?
2. What do you want to DO?
3. What do you want to HAVE?
4. Who do you want to SUPPORT?
5. What do you want to LEAVE?

Bonus: What is on your BUCKET LIST?

	BE	DO	HAVE	SUPPORT	LEAVE
MIND / BODY					
RELATIONSHIPS					
TIME / MONEY					
CONTRIBUTION					
ENVIRONMENT					
FAITH					
BUCKET LIST					

GROWTH MINDSET

Mindsets are ideas about oneself and one's most basic characteristics. There are two sorts: fixed and growth. Carol Dweck, a renowned psychologist researched and created the concept of mindset.

Individuals who embrace the fixed mindset hold these beliefs:

- They believe their fundamental qualities (such as intellect or talent) are unalterable and set in stone.
- These individuals will achieve less than their full potential because they avoid challenges, give up quickly, and regard their effort as fruitless.
- They don't appreciate constructive criticism or feedback and are afraid of the success of others.[2]

---

2   Peterson, R (2022) Entrepreneur Mindset $hift

Carol Dweck says "In a growth mindset, people believe that their most basic abilities can be developed through dedication and hard work—brains and talent are just the starting point. This view creates a love of learning and a resilience that is essential for great accomplishment." (Dweck, 2015)[3]

If we want changes to happen in our lives, we must believe that change is possible. We have to believe that who we are can grow and change. How we look at everything is affected by our mindset or set of beliefs. Think about how you relate to what happens around you. Do you see these instances as opportunities or as consequences? Do you think you have any say on how these things affect you and your life?

---

3   Dweck, C. (2015) Carol Dweck Revisits the 'Growth Mindset'

GOAL SETTING

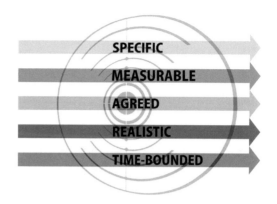

Based on everything you have written down and thought of so far, let's look at where you want to go. Take a few moments to write down where you want to be at the end of the year. Think about writing goals that are SMART (Specific, Measurable, Agreed/Attainable, Realistic and Timebound). These types of goals are achievable.

Example: I will reach a size 10 by June 1, by walking 30 minutes a day while listening to my daily reading.

What do you want to achieve?

1. Financially (income, giving, etc.): Think of this however best touches your heartstrings. What do you want to have accomplished when the year is over?

2. Physically (personal growth, habits to change, physical fitness): What do you want to be like at the end of the year?

3. Spiritually: Where do you want to be at the end of the year?

4. Emotionally: How do you want to feel about yourself, the world, your business, etc., at the end of the year?

5. Legacy: What do you want others to remember about you this year?

LIST OF THINGS TO ACCOMPLISH

I'm going to ask you to do this brain dump without second guessing your thoughts. Take a moment to think about anything and everything you should work on this year. Do not take any time, just jot down everything that comes to mind. You can list everything from small tasks such as daily journaling, to large tasks such as writing a book. Anything is possible. We are trying to write down all the ideas that are in your subconscious. We are not worried about the how just yet.

_____

_____

_____

_____

_____

_____

_____

Do it, Delegate it, Delay it, Dump it

Now looking back at your list of things to do this year, accept that it isn't realistic to work on all of them right now. Review these definitions and then sort them into these categories.

Do it (you personally need to work on now)

Delegate it (you can allow someone else to do, or are meant for someone else to accomplish)

Delay it (you need to work on personally but not right now)

Dump it (neither you nor anyone else needs to work on)

Action Matrix

Thinking of all you just wrote down and what you currently do...

What are the things you need to do to accomplish all you are setting out for yourself? Take a few moments to think of these questions and jot down what comes to mind. Don't worry too much over this, things might come as you continue working through your plan.

What do you need to STOP doing?

_____

_____

_____

What do you need to do LESS of?

_____

_____

_____

What do you need to KEEP doing?

_____

_____

_____

What do you need to do MORE of?

_____

_____

_____

What do you need to START doing?

_____

_____

_____

Habits for this year / tracker

Use this tracker to mark that you've done your priority tasks daily. You can gamify this by giving yourself points for each item. You can then share that with your accountability people and or reward yourself when you reach certain goals.

	Reading	Exercise	Journal	Work	Write	Family	Research		
1									
2									
3									
4									
5									
6									
7									
8									
9									

	Reading	Exercise	Journal	Work	Write	Family	Re-search		
10									
11									
12									
13									
14									
15									
16									
17									
18									
19									
20									
21									

	Reading	Exercise	Journal	Work	Write	Family	Re-search		
22									
23									
24									
25									
26									
27									
28									
29									
30									
31									

DREAM LIFE PLANNER • NOELLE L. PETERSON MED

WHO ARE YOU HANGING OUT WITH?

*"You become like the five people you spend the most time with.
Choose carefully."*
Jim Rohn

One of the best ways to plan well is to evaluate your support system.

Determine whether you're surrounded by the proper people; those who moti- vate, support, and push you to be your best. The aim is to spend more time with the optimistic people and supporters in your life and less time with pessimistic individuals and haters. It's good to revisit and make adjustments from time to time.

Begin by making a list of the individuals you hang out with. Take into account how your relationship with each of them affects you while looking at their names. Put a + next to those that energizes and inspires you, and - next to the ones that de-energize and discourage you! Make a deliberate effort to devote more time to the good relationships in life and less time to the de-energizing ones.

Identifying the positive and negative aspects of your relationships is a simple yet effective way to intentional about your relationships.[4]

---

4   Adapted from *Kim Perell's book: Ready to Jump: Your One Year Success Plan*

+ or −	Name	Notes How & when do you spend time? How is the relationship impacting your life?

DREAM LIFE PLANNER • NOELLE L. PETERSON MED

MY COMMITMENT TO ME

The idea of assessing your relationships is simple, but I completely get why it isn't easy to do.

After all, these are the people you hang out with. Even if they have a low rating in your evaluation, you care about them (or most of them). As a consequence, setting boundaries may be tough.

Let's make a strategy for how you'll create boundaries.[5]

I will stop… (examples: stop accepting bad attitude, not standing my ground, etc.)

---

5   Adapted from *Kim Perell's book: Ready to Jump: Your One Year Success Plan*

I will minimize… (examples: spending time with critical people, making excuses, comparing, etc.)

I will maximize… (examples: with people who encourage me, energize me, etc.)

Prioritize daily

Each day make yourself a priority list and a to-do list.

What are your top priorities for the day?

1.

2.

3.

What needs done today to accomplish your priorities?

1.

2.

3.

4.

5.

6.

7.

8.

9.

10.

Notes:

Daily planner:

Take time each morning to start the day off on the right foot. Use a 5-minute journal[6] or follow this plan.

List 3 things you are grateful for each morning:

1.

2.

3.

What needs done today:

1.

---

6   Based on the 5 Minute Journal from IntelligentChange.com

2.

3.

Your Daily I Am Statement(s):

1.

2.

Then each night, take just a couple minutes to evaluate your day. What were the wins of your day?

1.

2.

3.

What did you learn today?

1.

Your Dream Life

We can make things happen as we envision them. Think about what you want in life, what you who you to be. Use these statements to manifest your Dream Life. As part of your daily preparation time, write down and read aloud your "I am" statements regularly.

Describe in detail based on all the exercises you've done what your Dream Life looks and feels like.

_____

_____

_____

_____

_____

_____

_____

Now You Are Set

I hope you have completed these activities and have your SMART goals set, your vision board to keep you motivated and your "I am" statements to manifest your Dream Life. I would love to hear your story. You can find me on Facebook, Instagram and LinkedIn @n2r2peterson or at our website, AddValue2Life.com.

I encourage you to journal daily using the template in this book. Be grateful for what you have daily and celebrate the little wins.

If you struggle with any of these activities, journal your thoughts. Process what is going on. Are you afraid of something subconsciously? Write out what you are thinking and feeling, then go back and try again. I would love to work through this with you if you reach out.

About the Author

Noelle L Peterson MEd

Noelle grew up in Colorado as the oldest of four children. She grew up in the recession as her parents struggled to keep their dream home and raise their kids with the life they had planned. She grew up working hard and wanting to be the best. She wasn't popular at school, was always looking in from the outside, wanting more.

Noelle met her husband, Robert, in 1991 as she was learning how to adult. They have had more than 30 years of adventuring together. They have released two adult children into the wild. They love road trips, stock car races, and exploring off the beaten path. Together they serve as chaplains for their local stock car racing community.

They spent 10 years living in Latin America, learning Spanish in Costa Rica, and living and serving as missionaries in Bogotá, Colombia.

Noelle put herself through college while raising her own children and gaining valuable experience in the mission field as a missionary wife and volunteer teacher at the international school. She served in leadership and became a mentor as a missionary and then as a volunteer at their local church.

Noelle is trained in education, leadership, coaching and training. She uses her vast tool box to coach women in informal settings at work, church and through friendships.

With her years in ministry and leadership, experience as a mom and now grandma, Noelle offers a unique perspective guiding women to get out of their own way as she helps them see what is possible and that they are worthy.

Noelle and Robert launched Add Value 2 Life Coaching in 2018 to serve entrepreneurs. In 2021 they launched the Add Value 2 Entrepreneurs Podcast. Noelle is committed to helping women grow themselves to become the people capable of bringing their dreams to reality.

Noelle is the Ideal Speaker for Your Next Event

Noelle is an international speaker who has travelled and taught in English and Spanish. Her impactful message will inspire your audience and leave them ready to take action in their lives. She uses powerful stories of transformation to encourage everyone to add value. Her style will engage your audience and leave them ready to take action in their own lives.

Email Admin@AddValue2Life.com for more information.

Ready To Take Your Business to The Next Level?

Did you know that half of all businesses are closed within their first year, 80% are gone within five years and that 96% of all businesses fail within 10 years? That means that only 4% of all businesses last more than 10 years.

We know just how difficult it is to get a business off the ground. In 2018, Robert left a successful 20-year career in ministry to pursue his own journey of full-time, self-employment, so that we could do the work that we felt most called to do in this world.

We can tell you that those difficult times were definitely worth it. However, with that said, looking back from the perspective of knowing what we know today, we now realize that things didn't have to be quite so hard.

Starting a mastermind group changed everything for us.

We define a mastermind as "a small group of people who meet on a consistent basis, where every member of the group is 100% committed to the success of every other member in the group."

The concept of the mastermind was formally introduced by Napoleon Hill in his book, "Think and Grow Rich."

AddValue2Life.com/inner-circle-team

Ready to Hear More?

Entrepreneurs get stuck in their head, challenged by their thoughts, the voice in their head and their beliefs. We help them get out of their own way.

We chat with successful entrepreneurs who share their journey and the lessons learned along the way.

The show is fun and encouraging while maintaining a level of professional excellence. We talk business but we also ask about a favorite date night or how they spend their free time.

Add Value 2 Entrepreneurs is edu-taining, leaving the audience with actionable advice they can apply to their own work and life.

Our host Robert Peterson is a thinking coach focused on mindset, beliefs and manifestation. Our co-host Noelle Peterson is the heartbeat behind our company, coaching in leadership and process development.

AddValue2Entrepreneurs.com

AMPLIFLUENCE

AMPLIFY YOUR INFLUENCE

You're the Expert, but are you struggling to Monetize your Authority?

Amplify Your Influence in 3 Sessions

**Speak
Your Message**

**Publish
Your Message**

**Convert
Your Message**

Authors and Speakers often find themselves struggling to build a strategy that actually makes them money.

Check Out All Of Our 'Live' Tour Stops

amplifluence.com

SCAN FOR
TOUR INFO

More Books From

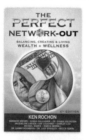

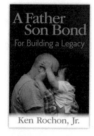

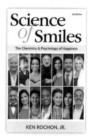

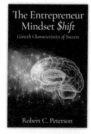
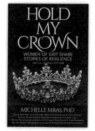

www.PerfectPublishing.com

Made in the USA
Thornton, CO
04/19/23 19:22:44

888ded0a-2f56-41c6-8be5-c909c017a8f5R01